Contents

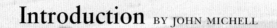

Introduction BY JOHN MICHELL

After some twenty years of crop circle research, no one yet has any idea of what is going on. Every season new and better designs appear in the cornfields. They are amazingly subtle and beautiful. Nothing in the world of art today has anything like their quality. And they have an effect on people. Those that study them are introduced to new subjects – to archaeology, geometry, number symbolism and the geography of southern England. Many people have been led by the crop circle phenomenon to a wider interest in life generally.

In the early days it seemed plausible that the circles were caused by freak whirlwinds or some other weather effect. That idea became impossible after 1990 when the first, elaborately-designed 'pictograms' appeared. These, obviously, were products of intelligent minds. So the theorists were divided. UFO enthusiasts believed the intelligent source to be extra-terrestrial, while most other people took the down-to-earth view that it was all a hoax.

The 'hoax' theory implies that unknown teams of skilled and dedicated artists are secretly at work during the summer nights, stamping or raking out large-scale patterns and leaving no evidence behind. That seems to be the only rational solution. Yet there are so many difficulties in it that experienced researchers are sceptical. No one ever detects these supposed circle-makers, or their cars or equipment. Certain fields are watched, yet circles suddenly appear in them, and nothing has been seen or heard.

Then there is the problem of how these large, complicated patterns could possibly be completed in the few hours of summer darkness, never left unfinished and never with awkward errors. Copyists have been commissioned to make their own circles, legally, in daylight and with no time limit. But none of these has anything like the quality of the great, unclaimed masterpieces that appear spontaneously.

My own rationalization is that the unexplained patterns are indeed of human design, but they are not made by human labour. I came to this through Steve Alexander's photograph of the hexagonal 'Koch fractal' design at Silbury Hill in 1999 (see Foreword). This revealed an internal pattern in the swirled-down wheat. It was not part of any practical construction-process, but seemed like a wave pattern developing from a centre. It was as if the figure had been transmitted from some source onto the wheatfield. Many of the recent designs indicate their maker's interest in fractal geometry. The source could, possibly, be extra-terrestrial, but I am more inclined to think that one of us is doing it. But I cannot think how it is done, nor can anyone else so far.

That is the general background to this book. Nick Kollerstrom, a teacher and mathematician, has studied the circle formations closely and for many years. If he has any belief about the identity of the circle makers, he does not admit to it. In the patterns themselves he has discovered the full range of figures and ratios that occur in the practice of geometry – the union of square and circle, the pentagon and golden section, the various polygonal constructions. In a natural and easy way, with no pain or compulsion, the circle-makers are introducing basic forms of knowledge that modern education barely covers.

1 Hypermaths

FOR THE SCHOOLCHILDREN OF TOMORROW

L et us imagine a maths teacher who could not endure the thought that Art and Science should be separate; and who demanded that Delight and Wonder should be the guiding principles.

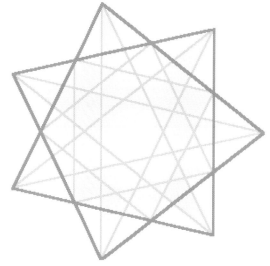

Hypermaths does not involve conic sections but only perfect circles, and deals with integers rather than decimals. Its study will therefore tend to produce more psychologically integrated and balanced individuals. In contrast with traditional maths, it deals with phi (the Golden Ratio) more than pi.

Whereas school maths traditionally aims to find the correct answer, Hypermaths aims to create the *mandala of wholeness*. Mathematics since Newton has been based upon procedures of analysis and abstraction, but the mandalas of Hypermaths seem to glitter with divine irradiations, as if perchance their study might make whole again our fragmented selves. They don't give an answer, but they awaken wonder. At times they say things simply, with the freshness of a new dawn. On the ground we see their constructions exact to a single blade of wheat, but cannot discern the pattern as it's too huge. Only from the air do we see the geometry, written on the ground.

Our lives are boxed in by squares and rectangles. Overcoming the tyranny of the right-angle, Hypermaths expands our consciousness through symmetries based on the three of the Trinity, the five of the magic pentagram, the six of the lotus Flower of Life and the seven of the mystic, unfathomable heptagon. Some impulse of delight motivates the unfolding of these forms, causing the pentagon and pentagram to interweave, and the Square, Circle and Triangle get together in forms we never dreamed of hitherto.

18 August, 1997
Hackpen Hill, Wilts

2 Vesica Piscis

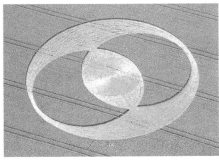

Wͤe experience the Vesica Piscis construction as a primal beginning of things, whereby One becomes Two. It is constructed from two circles of equal radii, each with their centre on the circumference of the other. This produces the square root of three, as the distance between their intersections, if the circles have unit radii.

The Circlemakers have given us a way to get a grip on this, by repeating the process twice, whereby the circle at the centre has to be one-third the size of that without. A double Vesica Piscis appeared, with the larger

23 July, 2000
Chiseldon, Wilts

one having a circle outside it and the smaller one, engraved within it, having a circle inside. We first notice that the 'eye' shape in the middle, the circle within has a radius half that of the arcs around it.

This construction uses the root-three proportion (equal to 1.73), shown by the cross-lines. It's bigger than the Golden Ratio (that's 1.62). If the outer circle has a radius of one unit, then the two major arcs have slightly larger radii, of $2/\sqrt{3}$. A second Vesica within the first one will have length $1/\sqrt{3}$ of its diameter. This means that the circle at the centre will have its radius one-third that of the outer one. The two arcs around the inner circle, making the 'eye', have radii double that, i.e. two-thirds that of the outer circle.

An early Hypermaths design from Fordham Place, Essex (of

unknown date) was analysed both by John Michell and astronomer Gerald Hawkins. Its middle 'bar' pointed due North. It was a 'geometrically coherent religious symbol,' Michell argued, based on the *Vesica Piscis*: 'the figure that emerges from the oZo form is the

nimbus of glory which surrounds divinities . . .' *The Cerealogist*, Spring 1991.

Michell's construction lines were those of a square plus an equilateral diamond or rhombus, which would make the small circles about one-sixth the size of the large circles of the *Vesica*. [From the trigonometry used here, this fraction comes to $(\sqrt{3}-1)/4$ of the large circles, or $1/5.5$]. This design's economical use of form points the way to the 'latent geometry' of later designs.

It is as if only part of the figure were inscribed upon the ground, Michell argued, in which respect it resembled the 'mason's marks' traditionally carved onto the stones they cut: 'A study of mason's marks shows that they too represent the cores of more elaborate geometries.'

A Twelvefold Vesica, and Diatonic Harmony
12 July 2000
Barnsley, Yorks

Rotating a Vesica around its centre in six steps here made a twelvefold mandala, with an outer circle having thrice the area of that within. In between there are 48 'squares' or rhomboids. To emphasise this number, an adjacent circle, of the same size as the inner one, has no curves but only a 7x7 grid of squares. The centre one is missing, to give a total of 48.

Discussing the matter with Gerald Hawkins, I asked him what was special about forty-eight? This was the master-number for the musical 'diatonic scale' he explained (white keys on the piano). English church bells peal out in these ratios, having no sharps or flats. He has argued that crop-circle diameters tend to be in these ratios (articles of his are cited at the back):

c	d	e	f	g	a	b	c'
1	9/8	5/4	4/3	3/2	5/3	15/8	2
24	27	30	32	36	40	45	48

The Circlemakers, claims Hawkins, are the first in the evolving history of mathematics, to point out the connection between musical tones and geometry. Let us hope he will further explain this matter. Gerald Hawkins has to tune his wife's lyre, so he has come to appreciate these subtle issues of musical harmony.

The design of this formation is similar to that of the Wiltshire 'Torus' of 11 July 1997, Marlborough, Wilts.

Ratio
late July, 1995
Roundway

Two circles of flattened corn have a gap between them. That gap gives the unit length that we start off with: doubling it gives the radius of the smaller circle, and trebling it gives that of the larger one. Thereby this formation plays with the 2:3 ratio. The thin-line circles (in the diagram by Peter Sorensen) reveal its hidden structure. A ring surrounds the design, and a total of eighteen of the gap-units span its diameter.

Binary Fission
28 July, 2001
Stanton St Bernard,
Wilts

Like a cell dividing, this new-millenium formation keeps on duplicating. Starting with the primal unity of a circle, it splits into two, halving its size at each step. This process ends up with thirty-two tiny circles, all in a line. Thereby a straight line emerges out of circles. This fission-process produces the sequence:

$$2^0 \quad 2^1 \quad 2^2 \quad 2^3 \quad 2^4 \quad 2^5$$
$$1 \quad 2 \quad 4 \quad 8 \quad 16 \quad 32$$

where the standing corn signifies even-number powers! I call this formation, *two to the fifth*.

3 The Triune Pattern

23 July, 1999
Meonstoke, Hants

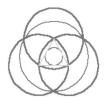

Crop circles or 'agriglyphs' often have a 'latent' or implicit geometry, that underlies the visible pattern. Their aesthetic beauty derives from the underlying structure. The 'Meonstoke' formation had circles of four or five different radii, and some kind of triangular pattern connects them.

We make the *Vesica Piscis* again, this time adding a third circle of the same radius, with its centre on the intersection-points of the first two. This creates a centre, from which we draw a larger circle, passing through the three intersection-points. Then a triangle is constructed in the centre, of sides equal to the main radii. The distance from the centre to a corner of this triangle equals $1/\sqrt{3}$.

There are some trig notes in the Appendices allowing you to check this. So altogether, the radius of the larger circle is ($\sqrt{3}$ - $1/\sqrt{3}$, or 15per cent more than the original circles ($\sqrt{3}$ = 1.73). Then, the radius of the small circle inside the triangle is $1/(2\sqrt{3})$, a mere 29 per cent of the original radii. The centre point cuts each of the three vertical height lines of the triangle in the ratio 1:2.

Web of Triangles
20 June, 1999
Pennyquick Hill, Bath

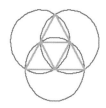

We can join up the triangles, which helps us to get a 'feel' for the construction. Here are four triangles in three circles, whose sides have the length of the circle radii. This circle also appeared at Corston, nr Bristol on 4 July, 1999

The Sphere Within
2 August, 1998
Wheely Down, Hants

Let's move on to a simpler design. Three crescent moons swirl around a small sphere at their centre. This formation is based upon the same three interlinked circles, and as before the small middle circle is defined by an unseen or 'latent' triangle. See if you can show (from the length of the triangle sides) that each of the three circles has its area twelve times that of the central circle.

Harlequin
1 June, 1997
Winterbourne Basset,
Wilts

The Harlequin requires ten circles of six different radii in its construction. At first it looks rather inscrutable and forbidding. But, as Hypermaths is concerned with *elementary* things, let's start with something simple. The figure shows two circles, and we sense a connection between the two. One is the central circle of Harlequin while the outer is that on which its three circle-centres are going to be placed. With a compass on the triangle corners, and radius set to the triangle length, intersections mark the big circle.

Q: *How do the radii of these two circles compare?*
A: *One is four times the other. If the inner circle has radius one, then the triangle has height three, and the outer circle radius is four.*

We first notice that the Harlequin has three circles which would each fit exactly inside its triangle. Using the earlier triune design, extend the three bisection lines out to touch the three circles, then join these points in a triangle. All these circles except the middle one have to *fade away*. Set your compass on a radius for a circle inscribed in the big triangle, then place it where the large circle intersects a bisection line, and draw the circle, or most of it. Repeating this will define a second centre circle, slighly larger than the first. That's it!

A tangent is a line that gently touches, without cutting. Here, three equal-sized circles nestled closely together in such a way that three tangent lines touched each of them. How does the distance between their centres compare with the diameter of the circles?

To answer this, one constructs the triangle as shown, whose height equals the circle radius. Readers may recall that, if an equilateral triangle has sides of 2 in length, then its height is √3 (you can refresh your memory on these things from the Note on Triangle Trig). Thereby we obtain the answer, that the centres are distant 4/√3 radii from each other , which means that they were separated by 15 per cent more than their diameters.

Tangents Touching
4 June, 1998
Cheesefoot Head, Hants

On 2 June, a triangle appeared within a double hexagon. The latter gave a twelvefold division of the circle, then the position of the triangle corners set up a twenty-fourfold division (i.e. 15° intervals). The lay within the triangle was very chaotic, which disturbed the first investigators. The next day, 3 June, the triangle had sub-divided into nine smaller triangles. The centre of the circle therefore had a sixfold division from these late-arriving triangles, to mirror the hexagon motif at the periphery. Also the edges of the triangles pointed to the spaces in between the two hexagons, emphasising the twenty-fourfold division of the circle.

The numbers twelve and twenty-four pertain to the totality of things. There are twenty-four vertebrae in the human spine, twenty-four letters in the Greek alphabet, twenty-four hours in the day and twenty-four particles of which Matter is composed. As the new

Triune Mandala
2 June, 2000
Silbury Hill, Wilts

millenium dawns, that is the present view of physicists: they found twelve fermions and twelve baryons, as the 'matter' and 'force' particles, with the former being composed of six quarks and six leptons.

The radius of the circle within which the triangle is inscribed is smaller than the outer circle by $\cos60/\cos30$, i.e. it is 89 per cent of its size. Thus the triangle touches the intersection points of the two hexagons. If 'a' is the radius of this circle, then the side-length of the triangle is $a\sqrt{3}$. (It may help to turn back to the earlier Vesica Piscis diagram here.) Then the side-length of the smaller triangles is one-third of this viz., $a/\sqrt{3}$, while their height will be half of 'a'.

It may help to construct a second triangle as shown, to give a Tibetan yantra-type effect. A circle has been drawn here which is about ten percent smaller than that around the original periphery. We saw earlier how the angle-bisection lines of a triangle cut each other in a 2:1 ratio, and the small triangles here show this. Their lines, drawn within the main triangle the day after it appeared, point exactly to the hexagon-intersections in the perimeter pattern, just as the main triangle stands on these.

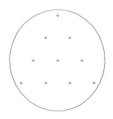

On his website 'Crop Circular', Freddy Silva commented on how this formation had '. . . its elements effectively encoding the harmonics of light – 3, 6, 9, 12, 24'. These are the overtones, as it were, that resonate within this formation. Removing the outer hexagons, and just leaving the points of the central triangle needed for its construction, gives the *tetraktys*, the sacred symbol of the Pythagorean order.

In the sky, Jupiter and Saturn were together, in fact they were conjunct within half a degree. This could be relevant: they meet every 20 years, and move 120° round the zodiac each time, thereby weaving out a big triangle in the zodiac. On this view, the double-hexagon pattern around the perimeter of this formation would be an allusion to the zodiac.

In this formation triangles were reverberating, as well as some star-hexagons. See if you can spot the triangles of scale-factors 1, 3, 5 and 7. It may remind us of Eastern-style 'Yantra' designs employed for meditation.

Triangle Yantra
18 August, 1997
Hackpen Hill, Wilts

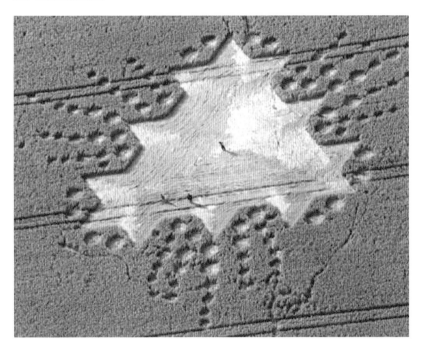

A rather charming version of the three-circles motif had a fourth circle cutting through their points of contact. Its area was just one-third that of the main circles, i.e. it was inscribed in the triangle joining their centres.

Circles Touching
25 July, 1999
Upper Beeding,
W Sussex

Here's an excruciating problem from the North of England, and it shows that cereal geometry isn't confined to Wiltshire.

Triangle Packing
18 June, 2000
Market Harborough,
Leics

Circles (or balls) have to be packed so that the three down the middle touch, that they touch horizontally in rows of three and five, and touch a surrounding equilateral triangle. What must be their relative sizes? It turns out that the three balls have to have radii 67 per cent of the large ball, and the five smallest balls, 55 per cent. I won't go over the derivation – it would lose too many readers! It isn't elegant like other Hypermaths problems, and requires approximation. There is a 'latent geometry' here, which the Circlemakers are quite fond of, an implied surrounding triangle has determined the figure.

Borromean Rings
24 June, 2001
Folly Barn,
Liddington, Wilts

The three interlinked rings appear in Renaissance and Mediaeval designs, known as 'Borromean Rings'. We start by constructing three circles in the usual way with their centres on the corners of an equilateral triangle. We then inscribe a circle within that triangle, and the smaller (incomplete) rings stand on that circle. Their radii are such that they intersect with the larger rings at the triangle corners. Two sets of circles thereby make the crescents, and their areas turn out to be in the ratio of seven to twelve. If we include the small circle at the centre, the ratios become 1:7:12, reminding us of the love of whole-number ratios which the Circlemakers have, although this time it's of areas rather than lengths. These are more subtle ratios than they were using a few years earlier.

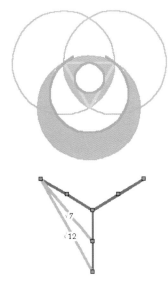

4 Squares and Cubes

Here's a theorem not in Euclid! We place a regular triangle in a circle, and add a square inside the triangle and circle, as shown; then the area of the circle is Pi times that of the square. The side of the square equals the radius of the circle. To make this construction, we divide a circle circumference by six. But, we must further subdivide it into twelfths for placing the triangle. See if you can show that the area of the top triangle is one-third of the whole triangle.

This design seems to suggest a door, leading into some house of mathematics. There is only one photo of this formation, by Lucy Pringle, but fortunately Andreas Muller measured its dimensions, enabling the construction here to be given.

House of Pi
25 July, 1998
Old Sarum, Wilts

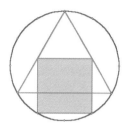

The Maltese Cross
4 August, 1999
West Kennet
Longbarrow, Wilts
16 July, 1999
Windmill Hill, Wilts

This was a fourfold *iterative* design. A large square has four smaller squares centred on each of its corners, plus twelve smaller squares centred on each of these secondary corners. Let's call these three square sizes Sq_1, Sq_2 and Sq_3. Their sizes were in the ratio of one, a half and a sixth, i.e. the scale factors were $Sq_1 \Rightarrow Sq_2$ as $\frac{1}{2}$ and $Sq_2 \Rightarrow Sq_3$ as $\frac{1}{3}$. These scale-factors made the total area of the formation just double, and its total perimeter was just treble, that of the main square. If a, b and c are the side lengths of Sq_1, Sq_2 and Sq_3, then the total area will be:

$$a^2 + 3b^2 + 9c^2 \text{ square units}$$

The figure has both *rotational* and *reflective* symmetry: if constructed on a computer screen, then one corner is built up, and the others made by quarter-turn rotations, or two reflections.

The figure seems to suggest some Asian temple floor-design. It had thirty-six large circles around its perimeter, at the points where another set of smaller squares would have appeared, had the iteration-process been continued one more time. In addition there were 120 smaller circles, thirty at each corner. We may not be surprised at twelves turning up here, since a fourfold shape was going through three stages of expansion.

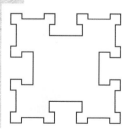

Cube with Sphere
17 July 1999
Honey Street, Wilts

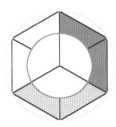

This was a notable 3-D figure, showing a cube with touching spheres both inside it and out. If the inner sphere has unit radius, then the cube around it will have sides of two units. How big would the outer sphere be?

Its radius would have to be $\sqrt{3}$ units, as we find by joining opposite corners of the cube and constructing a Pythagoras triangle.

Escher Cube
23 June, 1999
Allington Down, Wilts

A regular hexagon inscribed in a circle was divided into three diamond shapes or rhombi (rhombuses), which gave a marvellous 3-D illusion. So convincing is this illusion, that one may not at first notice the sixfold division of the circle, on which it is based. Three smaller rhombi appear within these (of which one is shown here).

The three smaller rhombi have just half the area of the larger ones. This means that their side lengths must be as the square root of two, i.e. as $1/\sqrt{2}$, to the main sides of the 'square'.

This formation makes us aware, in the most literal sense, of different dimensions. First we see a 3-D cube, then, with an effort, perceive it in linear terms as a regular hexagon divided into three; and lastly, we are startled to note a relationship of area: that the smaller rhombi of standing corn are half the size of the main ones.

Lino Floor Pattern
8 June, 1990
Exton, Hants

This early design had a 'latent geometry' that used four tangents, touching the circles as shown, and forming a square. One can develop this into a more complex lattice, of two square grids rotated at 45° to each other (Martineau, 1991), to give a regular octagon at the centre.

We thereby find the distance between the two circles: the centres of the small circles are twice the radius (of the big circle) from the formations's centre. The square root of two crops up quite a bit in this lattice-pattern. Thus, the sum of a

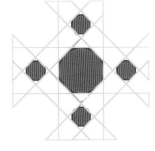

big circle and a little circle radius equals √2 times that of the big circle. Thus the little circles are √2 - 1 or 41 per cent that of the centre circle.

The picture shows the essence of the Chilcombe Down formation. The circles shown are touching each other. Let's set the big circle to unit radius, then we can show that the circle within must have radius $1 - 1/\sqrt{2}$. In a square with a diagonal, draw an arc from two corners to cut the diagonal. Then, if the large circle has a radius equal to the diagonal AB, the four circles have radii equal to the sides, and the small circle's radius is BC.

Chilcombe Down
1 August, 2000
Hants

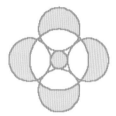

A corner of this formation is missing. This was because it was adjacent to a path through the cornfield, leading to the venue where a local rock band was playing that evening. Might its structure remind one of the four-four beat of this genre of music?

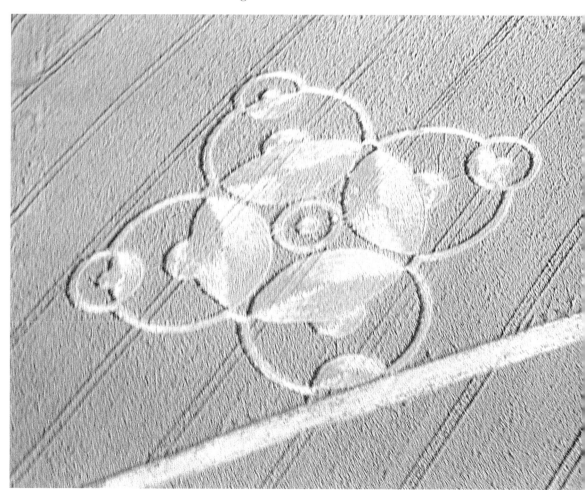

Squaring the Circle
7 July, 1997
Headbourne Worthy,
Hants

Described by Andy Thomas as a 'chunky quintuplet', this had four ringed satellites on the edge of a massive central circle. Their centres were at the corners of a square, whose area seemed to be the same as that of the main circle – as Michael Glickman noticed. Also, the area of these four satellite circles was equal to the central circle. The same area was thus being expressed in different ways.

Contact
12 June, 1995
Cheesefoot Head,
Winchester, Hants

This formation expresses a firmly established connection, by virtue of its strongly fourfold motif. The number four is to do with the solid structure of things. Lucy Pringle has called this formation 'the clutchplate'. Its inner circle is a quarter the diameter of the outer one – one sixteenth of the area – and in between them is a circle of half the outer diameter, so the three circles are decreasing in proportion. Two regular triangles will fit in between them, to demonstrate this.

Another ring, which has four smaller circles on it, is just double the area if the inner one (i.e. larger by the square root of two) which we can show by inscribing a square through the four circles, which just touches the inner circle. The lines of this square can pass through the sixteen smallest circles. In different ways, the number four echoes through this formation.

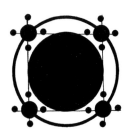

5 Pentagram and Pentagon

W e call the five-pointed star the pentagram, as traditionally used by wizards and witches. It is woven entirely from Golden Ratios (phi, Φ = 1.618, sometimes called the Divine Proportion), i.e. its sides are all in golden ratios to each other, so no wonder it had magic powers. If we inscribe a pentagram inside a pentagon, then the sides of the pentagram are phi times the sides of the pentagon, i.e. they are just over 60 per cent longer.

A beautiful formation appeared in 1988 at Goodworth Clatford, and does not seem to have been given a name. It featured on the front cover of *Circular Evidence* by Andrews & Delgado, which sold half a million copies. John Martineau showed why this design was attractive, in terms of its latent 'pentagram' geometry. If we inscribe a pentagram inside its outer circle, it defines the size of the central circle. The circle inside the pentagram is then $1/2\Phi$ or 31 per cent as big as the outer circle. This Golden Ratio proportion is repeated in the four satellite circles, which form the same ratio to the middle circle.

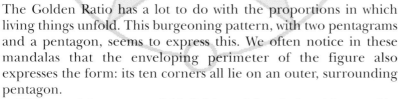

The Golden Ratio has a lot to do with the proportions in which living things unfold. This burgeoning pattern, with two pentagrams and a pentagon, seems to express this. We often notice in these mandalas that the enveloping perimeter of the figure also expresses the form: its ten corners all lie on an outer, surrounding pentagon.

The Double Pentagram
8 August, 1998
Beckhampton, Wilts

This mandala uses a tenfold division of the circle, with one of its pentagrams rotated a half-turn (36°, which we may here call a 'decile' angle, for one-tenth of a circle) with respect to the other. How much smaller must the smaller pentagram be, for their corners all to touch an (invisible) pentagon? A visible pentagon joins the corners of the smaller pentagram. In addition, can you detect a third, hidden pentagram, which defines the circle in the middle?

The circle in the middle indicates a *latent pentagram*. To show this, find the corners of the larger star-pentagon, and join them up to make another one, which will contain the middle circle.

As regards how much bigger the large star-pentagon is, compared to the other: this involves the cosine ratio of one-tenth of a circle, i.e. cos36°, which mysteriously enough turns out to equal half of the Golden Ratio, $\phi/2$, i.e. about 81 per cent.

Here's a hard question: *construct the 'latent pentagram' at the centre, as defines the circle in the middle. How much smaller is this, than the large star-pentagram?*

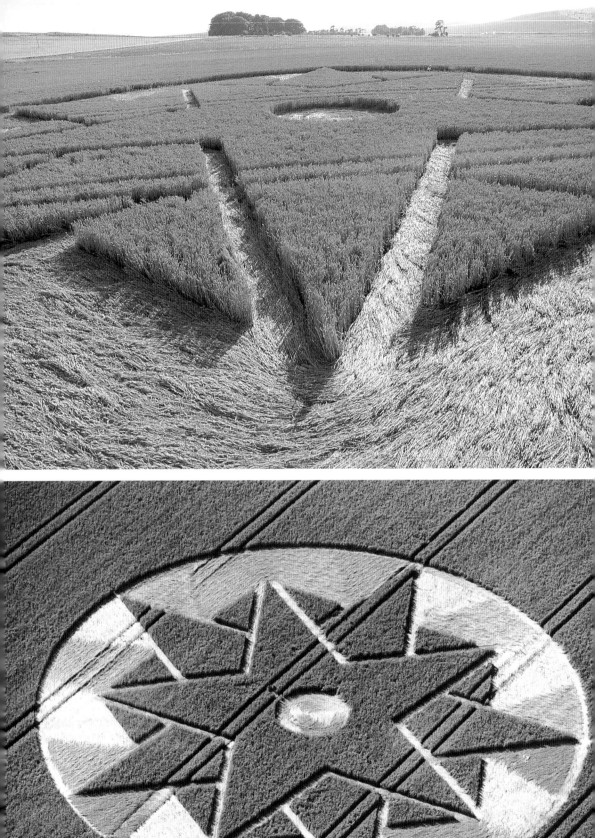

Answer: *they are in the square of the Golden Ratio, about 2.6 (cos $36°/\cos 72° = \Phi 2$).*

Can you spot five overlapping pentagrams? These turn out to be just half the size of the large star-pentagram, and are in a phi-ratio to the smaller one. Let's call the two pentagrams we started off with P1 and P2 where P1 is the bigger, then these five around the perimeter are P3 and the fourth tiny one at the centre, holding the circle, is P4. Can we now state their ratios? Let's try!

$$P1 \quad \Rightarrow \quad P2 \quad \Rightarrow \quad P3 \quad \Rightarrow \quad P4$$
$$\Phi/2 \ (81\%) \quad 1/\Phi \ (61\%) \quad 2\Phi\text{-}2 \ (77\%)$$

The pentagrams seem positively to burgeon, through these different sizes and rotations. Thereby we feel the connection of the Golden Ratio to growth-processes, especially of plants. We must surely thank the Circlemakers for making a mandala of such vibrant energy.

That was rather complicated. Let's try once more to grasp 'the geometry of life' through the Golden Ratio and pentagonal symmetry. Living things from flowers to sea-creatures burgeon with pentagrams, but they are absent from crystals. The planet Venus

A Nest of Pentagrams
24 July, 2000
Silbury Hill, Wilts

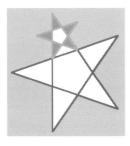

weaves out a double-pentagram in the sky every eight years. So how does the geometry work? Let's consider the series

$$1, \; \Phi, \; \Phi^2, \; \Phi^3 \; \ldots$$

It is a geometrical progression because each term multiplied by Φ, the Golden Ratio, gives the next, but each term is also the sum of the two previous ones (as with the Fibonnacci series.) This could be why Mother Nature likes using it; it allows living things to remain self-similar in their growth.

John Martineau's double-pentagram design (1995) for Venus' nearest approach to and furthest distance from Earth.

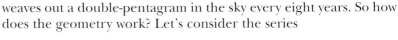

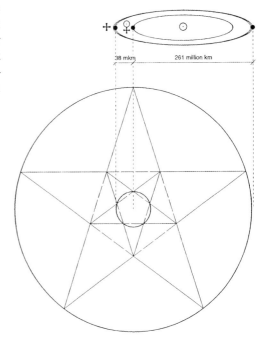

The design of this formation used three concentric pentagons, with a scale factor of Φ^2 between them. One starts with an outer, enveloping pentagon touching the outer circle, then a smaller one touches the corners of the centre star-pentagon, and finally an innermost one is framed within that. Its ratios go up as the square of the Golden Ratio, so that to construct it, starting from the centre, one marks out pentagrams expanding by 2.618 each time.

Not wishing to have too much symmetry, with all these 'perfect' Golden Ratios everywhere, the Circlemakers placed two errors in this construction, silently facing each other across the flattened wheat. On the one hand there was the kind of mistake you or I might make, with too much wheat laid down eroding one of the triangles. Adjacent to that, like some humorous zen paradox, was a triangle displaced, as if wrongly dropped . . .

Perched just outside the great circle of Avebury, this formation was described by Andy Thomas as 'one of the most striking formations of all time'. Groups did step forward to claim credit for it, but oddly enough they did not allude to its elegant double-pentagram architecture. This was only described by Gerald Hawkins a few years later (see the Crop Circular website). The outer circle and its two inner circles within the web bear the same ratio to each other, these being simple Golden Ratio proportions. The pentagram motif was echoed by the sets of five concentric circles drawn at ten points of the perimeter, which weave the 'web.' The design involves a twentyfold division of a circle.

Spider Web
11 August, 1994
Avebury, Wilts

This picture is by
Freddy Silva using
geometry by Gerald
Hawkins.

6 Sixfold Symmetry

This mandala used a twelvefold division of the circle. A star-hexagon is constructed of two triangles, then a hexagon is added, at a half-turn rotation with respect to it. The hexagon is scaled down in size, as if there were a second and invisible hexagon enveloping the perimeter of these two figures. This is characteristic of the Circlemakers. (The outer hexagon was traced out upon the flattened corn.)

Thereby the scale factor between the two hexagons must be cos 30° (thirty degrees being one-twelfth of a circle) or √3/2, which means that the outer hexagon is 15 per cent larger.

There are six diamond-shapes laid around the star-hexagon (of angles 60° and 120°). Can you show that the area of these diamond-shapes is altogether one-quarter that of the star-hexagon? And that the hexagon of standing corn has 9/8ths the area of the star-hexagon? Lastly, taking the diamond-side as unity, can you show that the large circle within the formation has a radius of √3?

Hexagon with diamonds
19 July, 1999
Devils Den

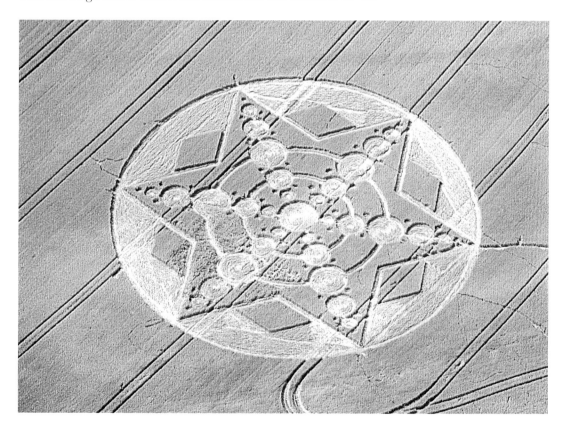

A Pentagram in Perspective
21 May, 2000
East Fields, Wilts

This formation shows a 'pentagram in hexagonal alignment' and, through its symmetry, 'the bipolar dark and light nature of life' (Freddy Silva's website). It is woven of triangles that are similar (30°, 60° and 90°). See if you can count 18 of these.

We inscribe a triangle in a circle, then mark out its centre by

three bisecting diagonals. This produces big triangles, and also medium ones. Then, a line joining two of these bisector lines produces the small triangles. The formation has a unique *axis of asymmetry*, which swaps over black and white upon reflection. Notice how this axis has been divided into four equal parts.

The triangle areas increase threefold at each step. The small triangles have their hypotenuse (long side) equal to R/√3 where R is the circle radius; the medium-sized triangles have their hypotenuse equal to the radius, and the large triangles have theirs as √3 R. The triangle side lengths thus step up in a geometrical progression.

The design looks a bit like a 3-D projection of a regular pentagram onto a flat surface, but it isn't: were this the case, it would have been inscribed in an ellipse, not a circle.

On the afternoon of 27 July , a coachload of Japanese visitors came to Beckhampton and meditated for a couple of hours, asking for a formation. It came! This formation, representing two intertwined Mobus loops, has been described as 'deceptively simple' by Michael Glickman. A half-turn in a joined-up paper strip makes a Mobus loop. It has only one side. The centre hexagon has width equal to the Mobus strips. There are tiny triangles in this design, six of which fit into the centre hexagon, the width of the strips being twice their height.

How long are the strips? Let's start off with the diagram shown, where the triangles in the corner are of two units and that in the middle, three. You may discern triangles scaled to 2, 3, 5, 7 and 9 such units. Thereby we compute that each Mobus strip has its length $6\sqrt{3}$ or 10.4 times its width. Try cutting out two such strips, to make this design. Admittedly, you may say, none of this looks like the real thing. A triangular grid, whose units are given by the tiny triangles, would be the best way to make it.

Japanese Origami
28 July, 1999
Beckhampton, Wilts

Hemp leaf
21 July, 2000
Pickled Hill, Nr Alton
Barnes, Wilts

Twelve circles make up this formation, with six of them cutting at the centre, and three strong axes of symmetry.

The Circlemakers have played endless variations on the sixfold 'flower of life' design over the years. Let's note that the characteristic one-sixth overlap is obtained when two circles of unit radii have a distance of *root three* between their centres. Why should that be?

The Dolphins
23 July, 1999
Barbury Castle, Wilts

There is a real euphoria in this unforgettable design. It employs three concentric circles in the ratio of 1: 3 : 4, where the outer two are as shown, and an inner 'unseen' one passes through the corners of its 'curved triangle'. To construct it, first make two concentric circles in the ratio 3:4, and then divide the outer one into six in the usual way. Draw spokes towards the centre from these points to meet the inner circle. With compass placed on one of the inner-circle points, extend it to reach an adjacent outer-circle point, on the sixfold division just made. Then draw an arc and do this three times.

Placing the compass on a corner of the 'curved triangle' thus formed, extend it to where one of the first intersects the inner circle, and draw in the secondary arcs.

Concerning the 'feel' of its triune quality, we note that: *The number Three is related to the idea of life, vitality and enjoyment, and hence to what motivates us and moves us to action.*

Mundane Astrology,' Baigent, Campion and Harvey, 1984, p.149

My impression is that these forms, which have never before occurred to anyone, would prove effective in mental hospitals, as a means of promoting mental integration and curing depression. Some of them I envisage as flower-bed designs for strolling around, but this one could be up on the wall, with some sort of lighting to show off its design.

N.B. the construction here given makes the three 'dolphins' too thin. The arcs had to be enlarged a little to give the final image shown, such that the maximal dolphin-width equalled the distance between the two circles. The Circlemakers seem here to have adjusted the arc-lengths for aesthetic reasons.

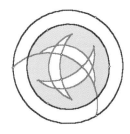

7 The Heptagon

Septile Angle
19 June, 1995
Cow Down, Andover,
Hants

An image of the septile angle (one-seventh of a circle, fifty-one and a bit degrees) here appears, comprised of seven 'bars'. The 'unconstructible' septile, the Great Pyramid slope angle, is here measured out. We also note that the inner circle has one-seventh the area of the main, outer circle, its radius being √7 of the larger one.

The Heptagon is not found in Nature. Mother Nature does not use sevens, which must be very much why the number has always enjoyed a mystic significance. The Heptagon (a seven-sided figure) cannot be constructed, using a compass and ruler. There is something rather hidden about it.

Dividing 360° by seven gives us a feel for its non-rational nature:

$$360 \div 2 = 180$$
$$360 \div 3 = 120$$
$$360 \div 4 = 90$$
$$360 \div 5 = 72$$
$$360 \div 6 = 60$$
$$360 \div 7 = 51.428571428571428571\ldots$$
$$360 \div 8 = 45$$
$$360 \div 9 = 40$$
$$360 \div 10 = 36$$

Taking the septile angle to the nearest arcsecond, as 51° 25' 43", this as a line of latitude passes through the dead centre of Avebury, as near as anyone can tell. Clearly, a Hypermaths course is concerned with geo-metry in this primordial sense. Half that latitude (1/14th) passes through the huge temple of Karnak within around ten arcseconds. The 1/14th division of the circle is quite important in what follows.

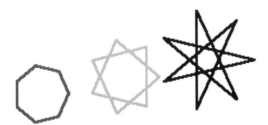

Let's meet the family of heptagons. Aren't they pretty? Their corner angles are n, 3n and 5n, where n is 1/14th of a circle. We will here call the second one an 'alternate heptagon', the third being the star-heptagon. Dividing a circle into seven, we join up adjacent points to make a heptagon, or join up alternate points going twice round to make an 'alternate heptagon' or join every third point to make a star-heptagon.

The Heptagon Sequence

Two of these heptagons were woven together by the Circlemakers in 1998. The diagram shows the essential pattern, and its silhouette appears in the inner pattern of standing corn. It uses a fourteen-fold division of the circle. The simple heptagon has been shrunk enabling an 'enveloping heptagon' to touch all fourteen of the corners – a technique quite often used by the Circlemakers. This inner pattern of standing corn has 28 sides of equal length, and three tiny circles run along each side, 84 in all (12 x 7). The interlinking heptagons form little rhombi whose sides equal those of the small triangles, and the sides of the alternate heptagon are just double those of the heptagon.

A Bi-Heptagon Mandala
8 August, 1998
Tawsmead Copse, Wilts

Q1: *By how much is the heptagon reduced, with respect to the alternate heptagon?*

A: *by cosine of 1/14th of a circle (cos (π/7) in radians), about 10 per cent.*

The outer perimeter used the same bi-heptagon design as found within, but filled-in differently. Within the laid-down corn, 'tracer lines' were found, depicting the heptagon-plus-alternate-heptagon together, but not rotated against each other by a fourteenth as before. These tracer lines are shown in Bert Janssen's diagram, here used with permission, and they connect together the inner and outer designs.

Q2: *How much smaller is the heptagon in the standing corn within, than that here traced out?*

A: *by cosine 1/7th of a circle (cos(2π/7) in radians), about 62 per cent.*

Q3 (Difficult): *By what scale factor is the alternate heptagon inscribed on the ground larger than that within the central standing crop?*
A: *by cos(π/7)/cos(2π)/7 or 45 per cent.*

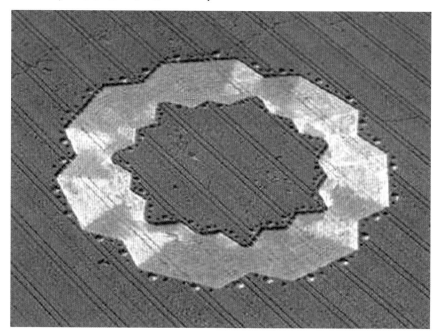

A Star-Heptagon
1 August, 1999
Roundway, Wilts

The logic of Tawsmead Copse reached an awesome fulfillment in 1999 with a concentric star-heptagon plus alternate heptagon, such that the shape of the latter also enveloped the overall design. As with the previous design, we can safely say that no one had ever conceived of such interlocking heptagons before. Circles were placed on all the corners (not shown), as if the heptagon corners needed to be covered up.

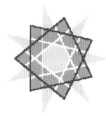

Q: *(Difficult) How much smaller was the alternate heptagon, than the star-heptagon?*
A: *cos (2π/7)/cos(π/7).*

Phew! That's a reduction to 69 per cent of the size.

I had only once seen heptagons combined together, before these: on a board designed for angel-communication by Dr John Dee, the Elizabethan magus. This was made early in the seventeenth century, and is now in the history of science museum at Oxford. It combined the three types of heptagon.

One can easily spend a year or two mulling over this design. I reckon it has been more thoroughly discussed and analysed than that of any other formation, in websites, books and articles (e.g. mine in *The Cereologist Summer 2000:* 'The Heptagon Family'). Of especial note is Bert Janssen's pioneering analysis, on the 'Crop Circle Connector' website, that of Martin Kietel (Finland) 'The Magnificent Seven' and (as usual) that of Freddy Silva in his most-visited 'Crop Circular' website. However much this formation is analysed, it retains its unfathomable presence, having all of the numinous qualities traditionally associated with the number seven. The same number of tiny circles line the inner structure as the outer perimeter.

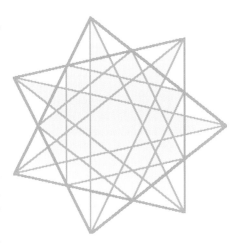

This enormous formation extended across eight or nine tramlines in the wheat. None of these passed through the centre of the formation, i.e. access to its centre was denied!

8 Fractal Form

Koch Fractal
23 July, 1997
Silbury Hill, Wilts

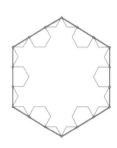

This design has six 'Stars of David' around its outside, with a seventh fitting into the middle. Its symmetry can be shown by an 'enveloping hexagon' which, placed around it, touches its 18 corner-points at equal intervals.

This formation shows a fractal process. Fractals are *iterative* which means that the process is repeated again and again. Because of this, a fractal form can have a finite area but an infinite perimeter. Back in 1905, Koch discovered his fractal of which the first few steps are here shown. It goes on doing its thing *forever*, which means that a fractal structure is supposed to look the same however much it is magnified.

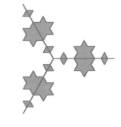

Let's start very simply with a straight line, to try to get a feel for the fractallising process. There seem to be two ways of applying Koch's discovery:

'If we take each of the three sides of an equilateral triangle as the base of a Koch curve facing outward, the result will be [what] Mandelbrot called a Koch island. Of course von Koch's curves could also be placed facing inward. In that case we get [an inside out Koch island].' (*Fractals*, H.Lauwerier, 36.)

The 'inside out' version turned up a year after the Koch island. It shows the very same Koch fractal process, only . . . somehow different. Mirror reflections are happening along its three axes. If Dr Who wants to reverse the polarity, this could be just the apparatus he needs!

Inverse Koch Fractal
16 August, 1998
Hackpen Hill, Wilts

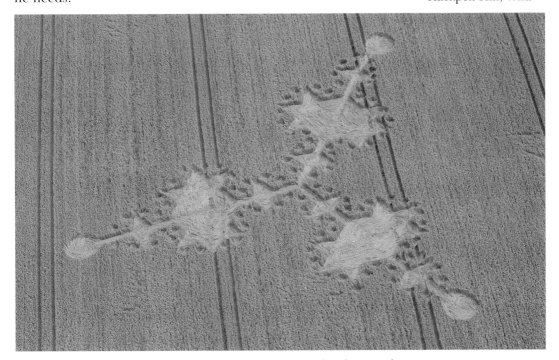

For addicts only: for the nth iteration of a Koch triangle, the number of sides = 3×4^n, its perimeter = $(4/3)^n$ for a triangle side of unity, and area = $1 + 1/3 + 1/3 \times 4/9$ . . . for an original area of unity. Only the last of these series converges, towards a limit of 1.6 of the area of the initial triangle. (By comparison, the enveloping hexagon is twice that area.)

The Koch Snowflake
8 August, 1997
Milk Hill, Wilts

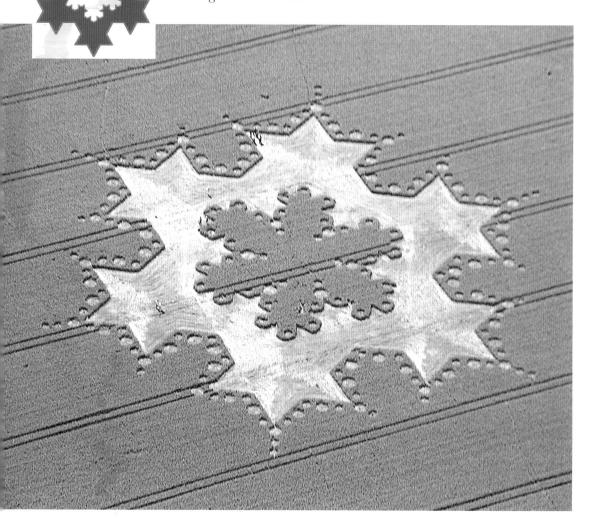

A supreme Circlemaker masterpiece, the fractal 'snowflake' of Milk Hill (just south of Avebury), had an inner structure reflecting its outer design, although enigmatically different. We have seen that Von Koch discovered how a fractal process developed along a bar or line, and how applying this to the three sides of a triangle gave the 'Koch snowflake'. A hexagon is now placed within that triangle, with three of its vertices touching and bisecting the triangle sides. Six Koch-fractal bars are required, compared with only three for the outside. They are scaled to fit onto the sides of the hexagon, facing inwards. That's it!

The formation has six axes of symmetry. Its construction is an exercise in the basic transformations of reflection, rotation and enlargement.

Hexagon-stars can be fitted around the 'pattern within' of the Koch Snowflake. A merry ring of dancing stars will form its silhouette. See if you can show that these stars are each one-twelfth the area of those we looked at earlier. (Hint: use the diagram of a hexagon in a triangle that we used for its construction, and show that the sides of the hexagon within are $1/2\sqrt{3}$ those of the triangle.)

Starting off from a 'Star of David', six stars one-third of its size fitted around it, each touching the others, to give the 'Koch fractal' design of July 1977. The 'Koch snowflake' design of a month later can be viewed as having 18 such stars touching each other around its inside. Here the scale factor was more complex, as they were reduced by $1/2\sqrt{3}$.

Sierpinsky Sieve
16 June, 1999
Chilbolton, Hants

Divide a triangle into four and throw away the middle bit. One keeps on doing that, going smaller and smaller, keeping on *forever*. In contrast with the previous fractal, its area grows ever less, as it becomes hollowed out. Its area will be $3/4^n$ of the original triangle for n iterations. The concept was found by the Polish mathematician Sierpinsky in the 1920s. However much it is magnified, the structure of the Sierpinsky sieve will not change. The formation showed the second step, whose 'area' would equal $(3/4)^2$ of the original triangle. The Circlemakers have added a mirror-reflection to the Sierpinsky Sieve, to give an extra degree of symmetry.

If one constructs a 'Pascal's triangle' and then marks its even numbers white and its odd numbers black, then, oddly enough, it gradually turns into a Sierpinsky Sieve. Does Nature use fractals? Experts believe that fractal-like processes tend to occur in violent situations where strong, turbulent forces need to be damped: such as the surf-pounded coastline, the blood vessels of the heart, and the wind- and rain-buffeted mountain.

9 Spirals

DNA
17 June, 1996
Alton Barnes, Wilts

The superb 'double helix' formation of 1996 had quite a 3-D appearance in its use of perspective. Mathematically, it comprised a sine plus a cosine waveform, each going through two cycles. There was a *phase difference* between them of 90°.

DNA rotates as a twisted ladder by one-tenth per step, or ten 'rungs' for a complete rotation. As we have ten fingers, so the Molecule of Life revolves in ten steps, an angle subtly connected to the Golden Ratio. An isosceles triangle whose top angle is one-tenth of a circle, mysteriously has its sides in the Golden Ratio. The 'DNA' formation

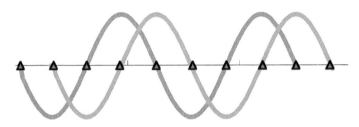

reminds us of these special properties. Its structure wove through ten circles in a row.

By its 3-D appearance, the 'DNA' formation shows a 'left-handed' or anti-clockwise twist. You may wish to get out a corkscrew and look at it! All human DNA is right-handed, i.e. it turns clockwise. The 3-D-looking formation on the ground in 1996 depicted a *mirror-reflection* of our DNA structure. Clearly, this is something to reflect upon . . .

Chemists have come to appreciate how important left- and right- handedness is for molecules in living things. Thus, the difference in smell between oranges and lemons is due to the same molecule, but in left- and right- handed forms. Asymmetry is built into life. All human DNA must twist in the same direction, for reproduction to be feasible. One could imagine a world where it was the other way round . . .

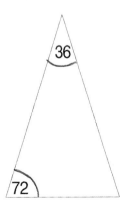

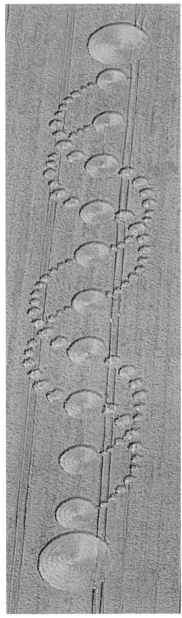

Triple Spiral
29 July, 1996
Windmill Hill, Wilts

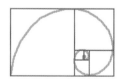

What are called *geometric* spirals appear in living things like sea-shells and sunflowers. They contain an infinity within, as the spiral goes on forever, never quite reaching its centre. They are the only shapes which never change, however much they are enlarged or shrunk. Let's start off with the Golden Ratio spiral, which contracts (or expands) by a fixed *ratio* for a given turn at the centre: it increases by Phi the Golden Ratio (61 per cent) per 90°. One can make these spirals (readers may dimly recall) using Fibonacci number sequences. The sea-shell of the Nautilus is a well-known example of this curve. The curve is also known as a 'logarithmic' spiral because one needs logarithms to construct it.

Checking out the Windmill Hill spiral of 1996, using Paul Vijay's diagram, I found that over the main bulk of the formation the three arms were genuine spirals. Mathematically speaking, a geo-metrical spiral has its tangent making a constant angle to the radius vector, i.e. the line coming from the centre. If one joins up any part of the spiral by a line drawn to the centre, the angle it makes with

that line mustn't change. That is why the geometric spiral is the only shape that remains the same regardless of size: however much you magnify it, it still looks just the same!

The Windmill Hill spiral had its three arms expanding according to the *square of the Golden Ratio* per 90° turn, (that is 161%, as $\Phi^2 = \Phi+1$). This glorious triple-spiral thus has a connection to the Golden Ratio. It wasn't a 'Julia set' (as widely called) but a triple spiral. By contrast, a spiral-like 'Julia fractal' which had appeared next to Stonehenge two weeks earlier had

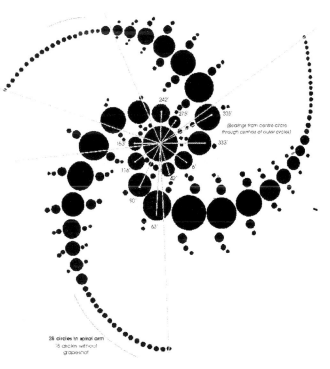

242°

275°

305°

(Bearings from centre circle through centres of outer circles)

153°

333°

6°

186°

12°

90°

63°

28 circles in spiral arm
6 circles without
grapeshot

Spiral Mandala
13 August, 2000
Woodborough Hill,
Wilts

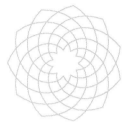

a central line through it which did not maintain anything like an equal angle to its radius-vector, i.e. it wasn't a spiral, mathematically speaking.

2000 was the first year in which 11-fold cereal geometry appeared, just as 9-fold geometry first appeared the previous year. This could be related to the sunspot maximum of that year, the peak of the 11-year cycle. The solar magnetic field reverses every 11 years, making a complete cycle in 22 years: this is the heart-beat of our solar system.

To make this formation, one divides a circle into *forty-four* equal sectors, that is 8° 11' at a time. These divisions expand out through fourteen concentric circles, or 15 including an outer one. Each concentric ring has twenty-two triangles, so that the 44-fold division is required to find the apex of each triangle. The rings were all equally spaced, so that all triangles had the same height. The triangles around the innermost ring are equilateral, then they grow more flattened towards the outside edge.

There are two types of spiral, logarithmic and Archimedes, and we've already looked at the first kind. The one expands by an equal ratio per angle at the centre, while the other expands by an equal

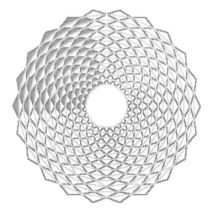

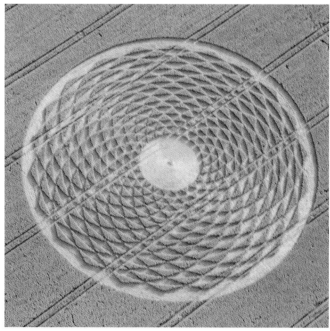

amount per angle at the centre. It's this second kind that now concerns us. If Θ is the angle at the centre and r is the distance from the centre, then in an 'Archimedes spiral' r increases by an equal amount per equal-angle turned at the centre. The equation making these spirals was:

$$r = \pi\Theta/22, \quad \text{where} \quad 4 < r < 19$$

– a lot simpler than that for a geometric spiral!

We start by putting the radius equal to four units, then rotate one forty-fourth of a circle (half a triangle width) for each unit increase of radius. Let's be clear that these Archimedes spirals don't use ratio* – they are purely arithmetic.

Constructing the the Archimedes spirals in this way, going out to the periphery and then returning, then going out again, without removing the pen from the paper so to speak, we find that an 11-fold structure results. Somehow, one gets a rather sacred feel about it. You or I wouldn't quite think up such a design. The complete mandala comprised two of these, one rotated by one twenty-second of a circle with respect to the other.

Finally, we take just one pair of these spirals, and extrapolate them back to the centre. The geometry of the heart is revealed. What can one say? There is a kind of perfection in these works of the Circlemakers. This mandala appears as having been woven of twenty-two 'hearts'.

10 Others

A Ninefold Star
18 July, 1999
Cherhill, Wilts

Three equilateral triangles are interlinked, so as to produce nine small triangles. These are not right-angled: one angle is 40°, one-ninth of a circle, and another must be 60° as the main triangles are equilateral, leaving a remaining angle of 80°.

Six crescent moons move around, within. A week later another ninefold design appeared (29th July, Stantonbury Hill near Bristol) again having a large crescent Moon design right next to it. This suggests that the Circlemakers are linking the number nine to the nine moons of gestation, i.e.

$$9 \times 29.5 = 266 \text{ days}$$

as the mean period from conception to birth.

Standing at the corners of these enormous triangles, I saw no trace of any pole having been used, or weight or of footprints. Robin Heath said to me, 'If I had ten surveyors working for me, I wouldn't be able to make that in a field, in one night.'

A gigantic formation of 1999 spanned no less than eight sets of tramlines in wheat. It received a bad press, with a *Daily Mail* story that it was 'hoaxed' i.e. man-made. That story eventually fell apart, but it impeded appreciation of the formation. Articles by both Francine Blake and Lucy Pringle described how the formation appeared on a clear full-moon night, on a hillside facing into the village of Avebury, with witnesses about till 3 a.m. who saw nothing; and that the journalist only arrived two days later to construct the story. The crop was sparse, the soil eroded and the lay was rough, so no-one seemed pleased with it. Perhaps such an illusory tale, where even the journalist who wrote it could not be located, was part of its subtle message, where things were not what they appeared to be. The formation depicted a *two-tier* optical illusion.

A triangular lattice of thirty-three circles was made, and by lines within the circles a 3-D illusion of cubes was generated. 'Missing' corners to the cubes conveyed the impression of which cubes were in front and which, behind. Then, before our amazed gaze, six of these cubes set up the illusion of the impossible 3-D 'tribar' shape. This shape was described by the British psychologist R.Penrose in 1958, and its principle was much developed by the Dutch artist M.C.Escher. Altogether the formation had five 'levels' of organisation: it showed the 'tribar', built out of six cubes conjured up from 33 circles, these being held within a triangle inscribed in a circle.

Spirit of Escher
29 July, 1999
Avebury, Wilts

The Compass Rose
25 August, 1998
Avebury, Wilts

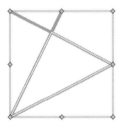

A little-appreciated eightfold design turned up in 1996. An octagon at its centre was *asymmetric* and not a regular octagon. The design is composed of four 'Pythagoras' 3-4-5 triangles. Rotating such a triangle about its centre through three square-turns would make it (ignoring the pattern at the centre). All of its corners touch an *enveloping square*. Would any other triangle do this? This is a familiar signature of the Circlemakers.

If a rope is divided into eight equal sections by knots, then eight people each holding one corner should be able to make this design. It would help to have a square marked upon the ground, whose sides were half of these lengths, to weave the octagonal shape.

Let's say that the square at the centre has sides two units, then we soon see that the triangle sides are 3, 4, and 5 units. We notice that eight smaller but similar triangles cluster around the central square. These turn out to be six times smaller than the main triangles.

We notice two squares at the centre. There is a rotation angle between them of arcsine $3/5$, which is close to one-tenth of a circle, about $37°$. The 'enveloping square' around the perimeter would have an area just five times larger than the centre square. We could instead view the formation as composed of four rhombi, of two kinds, where the smaller one has an area 3:2 of the centre square.

Suppose we start from that enveloping square around the perimeter. Eight points are marked upon it as shown, then joining up every third point will make this shape. This bring us back to the puzzle we started off with: why should joining up a square, in this way make a 3:4:5 triangle?

Octahedron
23 June, 1999
West Overton, Wilts

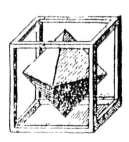

This is the surface map of a 3-D diamond. Fold it up to make an octahedron, one of the five 'regular' solids.

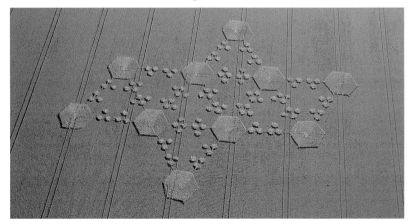

A sixteen-fold division of the circle was the basis of this eight-pointed star (as Michael Glickman pointed out). Each of its sides pointed to a 5/16ths rotation. This had the effect, that after three steps one was almost back to the start position, but subtly moved around one-sixteenth. It takes 48 steps to return to one's starting-point!

   This may be irrelevant, but the formation appeared on a day of the Sun and Venus meeting in the sky, and Venus does go through its motions in an eight-year period.

Star-Octagon
11 June, 2000
Silbury Hill

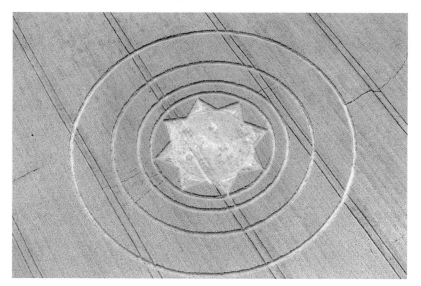

Golden triangles were woven into a 3-D -type illusion, a perspective view of a hexagon. It had a square at its centre as the key to its design (no ground measurements could be taken).

   There are six triangles here of laid corn. They are all equal, and because of this we can see that their base angle must be that whose tangent is three, about 72°. This is the triangle whose sides are in the Golden Ratio (see Appendix).Thus, this formation has two interlocking 'golden triangles'. The ratio of laid to standing corn area in the hexagon-shape is two to one.

Two of these three circles touched each other's centres, and the smaller two were in the Golden Ratio to each other. The largest however was not of quite the size it should have been to continue this progression. The smaller circle overlay the bigger one each time, and there was no access to their centres.

Hexagon Brooch
22 August, 1999
Upavon, Wilts

A Golden Chain
23 June, 2000
Sibson, Cambs

Asteroid Belt
26 June, 1995
Winchester, Hants

This rather charming depiction of the inner solar system showed the planetary orbits as thin rings of standing wheat, about a foot wide. To evaluate it one needs (I suggest) concepts of planetary orbit radii and eccentricities, perihelion (from 'helios' sun and 'peri', near) as the orbit-position closest to the Sun, Ceres as the largest asteroid, and, finally, of heliocentric planetary longitude. That these should be required to evaluate some flattened wheat in a cornfield is remarkable.

Yes, Earth is missing . . . but the positions of the inner planets are shown, together with Mercury's perihelion position. Around the perimeter was a pretty ring of asteroids. Did the planetary positions define one particular moment – when it formed (as claimed by J.Rasool: Andy Thomas, *Vital Signs* 1998)?

Let's start with a diagram of the relevant planets at the time of its formation against a sidereal zodiac, so that the starry constellations are behind these signs. Mercury's perihelion lies in the stars of Taurus as shown, while Venus was then at two degrees of Taurus. The crop formation doesn't quite show these as the right way round! But, Venus and Mars are correctly positioned.

In the heavens, one sees while facing South the zodiac constel-

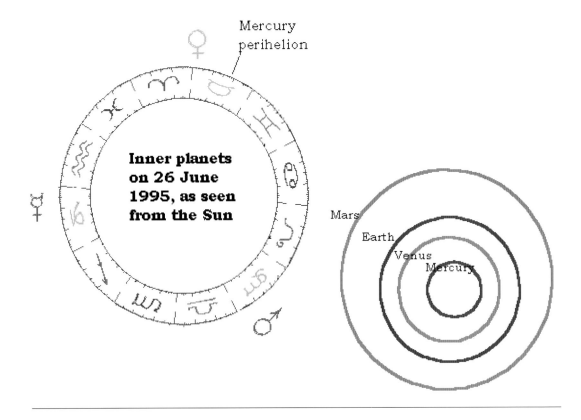

Mercury perihelion

Inner planets on 26 June 1995, as seen from the Sun

Mars
Earth
Venus
Mercury

lations arched across the sky, such that Taurus is to the right of Aries, and thus the familiar sequence moves round clockwise. That is the way this zodiac circle is here represented.

The orbits given in this formation of the inner planets plus Ceres, the biggest asteroid, are remarkably 'true'. Mercury's orbit is highly eccentric, whereas Venus' orbit is almost perfectly circular. Earth's is fairly circular too, coming about three per cent closer to the Sun at our perihelion (in midwinter). Mars' eccentricity is also indicated in the diagram. The radii of the circles representing the planets are remarkably accurate, especially if the distance of the asteroid belt is taken into account, as the graph shows.

This formation contrasted the closely circular orbits of Earth and Venus, with the far more elliptical orbits of Mars and Mercury. It correctly depicted five different relative distances from the Sun, and the degrees of eccentricity of the orbits involved. Finally, it showed fairly well the heliocentric positions of the Sun and three planets around the time of its formation.

During the 1990s astronomers have discovered many new planets in other star-systems, but all with far more eccentric orbits than the planets of our solar system. So, perhaps this formation is telling us that there is, after all, no place like Earth.

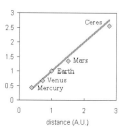

A 1995 crop circle copied for the film, *A Place to Stay.*

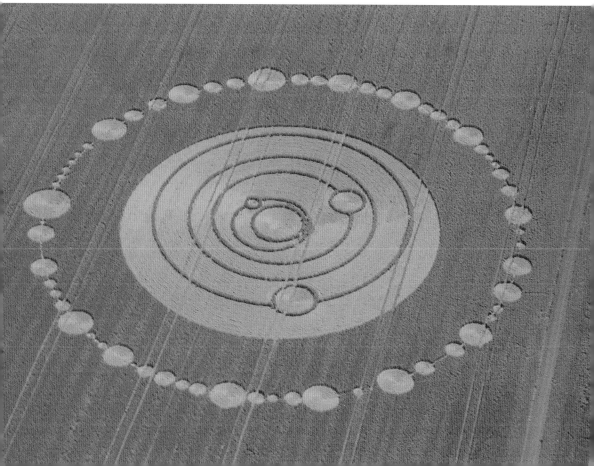

Lunar Month
(not shown)
4 July, 1997
New Cheriton, Hants

The Circlemakers are enchanted by Selene's sphere and never tire of depicting its phases and meetings with the Sun. One could not count the formations on this theme! There was a small and little-appreciated formation showing the twenty-nine days of the 'synodic' lunar month, as marks its meeting with the Sun. The average length of the female cycle is also of this length: twenty-nine days (and not twenty-eight, as one often hears cited).

From each side, faint dots cascaded towards the centre, indicating the maximal *influence* of Luna on the Earth, twice a month. Tides are then highest, at Full and New moons, and, who knows, perhaps more subtle influences are also at work.

Moons in the Year
15 June, 1995
Danebury,
Nr Andover

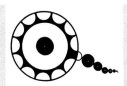

There are on average 12⅓ lunar-month cycles each year. A struggle used to go on, in the endeavour to relate the lunar months to the solar year. Every third year or so an extra 13th mo(o)nth has to be added in, to keep the months and years moving along in synch.

There was a 'solution' to this given by the Circlemakers, with 12 half-moons in a circle of the solar year, and a gap signifying the days left over. Next to this were seven dark rings. What were they for?

The Metonic cycle of 19 years links together the year and month, and has been used for thousands of years to compute the calendar. The technique is that 12 of these years have just 12 lunar months in them, then the remaining 7 each have a 13th month added in. That keeps them in step. We could write 'Meton's equation' as:

$$\text{Year} \div \text{month} = 12 \, \tfrac{7}{19}$$

The two sacred numbers 12 and 7 thus appear in this formation, a pleasant image of the Metonic Cycle.

Sidereal Moon
29 June, 1997
Meon Valley, Hants

The Moon orbits around Earth just over thirteen times each year, in its 27 day 'sidereal' cycle. Here the equation is $365 \div 27.3 = 13.4$, and the diagram does show just this amount. It moves 13 times faster than the Sun in the sky, and covers 13° of the zodiac per day. Thus the lunar number 13 reverberates through folklore and ends up as the unlucky number! The Sleeping Beauty fairytale starts off with a King who has to invite the 13 wise women to his daughter's baptism, but only had 12 golden plates . . . the 13th was left out, and so became 'unlucky'.

**A Twelvefold
Mandala** *(shown)*
1 July, 2000
Castle Down, Hants

The twelve moons of the year here appear in a symmetrical mandala-type composition. The number twelve here signifies psychic integration and wholeness. The lunar month is often depicted as an eight-stage process, shown here in the centre. For

the mandala-concept, see the illustrations in volume nine of Jung's *Collected Works*. Painted from dream-images, they are remarkably evocative of the crop-circle designs.

The 'Beltane Wheel' appeared as a powerful solar image, in a yellow field of oilseed rape (whose stems are thick and difficult to bend). It came on the day of Beltane in the early morning: 33 revolving tongues of fire. Beltane was the traditional fire-festival heralding the start of Summer, as the Sun reached 15° of Taurus (midway between the Vernal Equinox and midsummer (at 0° of Aries and Cancer, respectively).

Beltane Wheel
4 May, 1998
Silbury Hill, Wilts

Its location was precisely due North of Stonehenge, Britain's primary solar temple. Avebury is itself closely due North of it, about two degrees East of North, but this site was spot-on due North of Stonehenge.

Every 33 years, there appears a close synchrony between day and year. To show this, multiply the length of the year (365.2422 days) by 33, and the remainder comes to a mere 11 minutes, while other numbers will give much bigger remainders. The days and years will roughly coincide every four years, which gives the leap-year adjustment, but very exactly they synchronise over this longer period. So 33 is a solar number. This is why, Robin Heath has argued, the 'solar hero' Christ was supposed to have lived for that many years. This calendar-principle was discovered by the Persian astronomer Omar Khayam in the 14th century. It is used to the present-day in the Chinese calendar, but not so well appreciated in the West.

There are fundamentally two solar numbers, both in years. The number of the heart-beat of the Sun is 22, composed of two 11-year sunspot cycles; then, in addition, there is the 33-year calendar-period.

Muslim readers may take a different view of the number 33 because the lunar months of their calendar move round the solar year. And how long do they take to move once round? Why, they take 33 years. The feast of Ramadan moves once round the four seasons in 33 years (subtract twelve times 29.53, the lunar month, from the solar year leaving ten and a bit days; dividing which into the year gives 33 as the nearest integer).

The lunar year used by Muslims is shorter than our solar year by just this amount. This formation can be seen as a kind of gear-wheel in which every 33 of our solar years, the Muslims get one extra! Thus Hypermaths creates a point of dialogue between Muslims and non-Muslims.

12 The Plot Thickens

Vertigo Wheel
14 July, 2000
Bishops Sutton, Hants

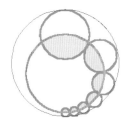

*S*omebody had fun constructing this one, as if illustrating some gravity-defying apparatus. Mathematically, it is a study of ratio. The centres of 12 touching circles are on a ring. There are seven circles of ascending size, the biggest one six times larger than the smallest. You or I might have made them increase by a given ratio at each step (see below), but the Circlemakers made that ratio *itself increase* at each step, which gives a more organic feel to the sequence. The big circles are increasing in size by a larger proportion than are the small circles. Plotting their sizes, only the logarithm *of the logarithm* gives a straight line (see graph). Well, that's something new! We could call their method, accelerated ratio.

Next, this seven-step sequence is placed on a circle, so their different radii have to be computed in relation to the main circle. I'd call that a university-level maths problem. Then the whole design is mirror-reflected, shrunk and displaced so as just to fit inside without touching! This helps to keep the design in balance.

The Circlemakers have a penchant for having a containing figure on the perimeter, an unseen presence which gives form and enhances the aesthetic appeal of the design. In this instance it's a

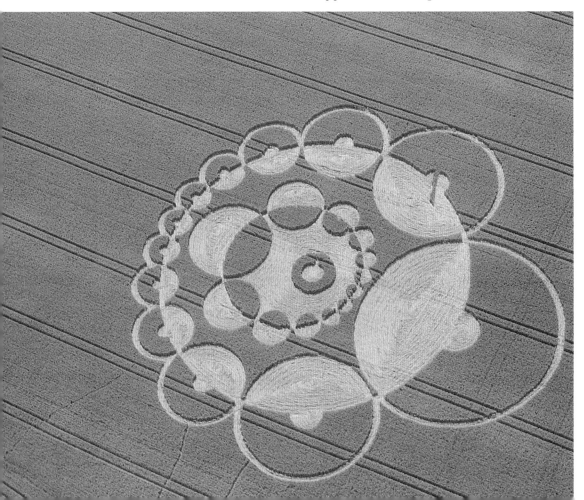

circle. These 12 circles are all contained within an out-lying circle, more or less. The two on either side of the biggest circle don't quite reach it. The 12 circles stand on a visible circle and touch an unseen circle. Their centres stand on a common circle, they touch each other, and they touch an eccentric outer circle. This can safely be described as the most complex maths problem ever inscribed in an English cornfield!

Putting the maths aside, let's consider a more important matter. Supposing that you, gentle reader, were approached over some civic design, say a shopping precinct paving, which pattern would you choose? I'd say there is a case for using this one, or at least its core design, perhaps with a fountain in the middle. The essence of this formation is a *13-circle* design, with 12 circles a-whirling – they are definitely whirling – around a 13th.

A 'Moiré' interference pattern caused widespread amazement. 'Perhaps the most extraordinary crop formation in history' was Freddy Silva's comment. One could not recognise its design from the criss-crossing patterns at ground level, but (at least in principle) it turned out to be fairly simple. A circle is first divided into 60, at 6° intervals. This may remind us of the use

Magnetic Field
22 July, 2000
Avebury Trusloe, Wilts

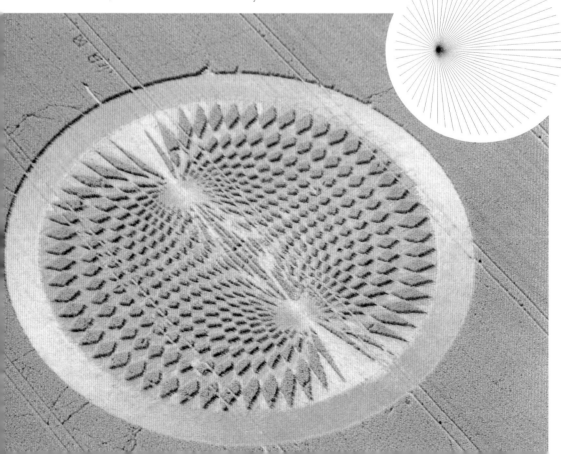

of base-sixty arithmetic in antiquity, by those who first divided up the circle into degrees.

These 60 points are then drawn to a focus midway between the centre and periphery. A mirror-reflection then creates a second focus, which interferes with the first one. The pattern produces, as can be seen, two sets of 29 corners. One may be reminded of the 29 days in the lunar month, as the formation was adjacent to Avebury, with its large ring of 29 stones.

Arriving on the day after its formation, I carefully searched for evidence of poles, pikes or whatever having been placed at the ends of the long straight lines, or at its two foci, but found none. It is worth comparing its design to the quite similar Moiré pattern given in *Mosaic and Tesselated Patterns* by John S. Wilson (1983). Thereby one can appreciate how the Circlemakers constructed a circular mandala out of a well-known interference pattern.

The formation was seen by many to resemble a huge magnetic dipole. It was in this very formation that Mr Colin Andrews was filmed by the BBC (7 August), promoting his new 'magnetic field' theory. Brandishing an electrostatic voltmeter, he declared that no magnetic field was here detectable, and that, hence, it was man-made. Did this show a sense of humour of the phenomenon?

The Mandelbrot
1 August, 1991
Ickleton, Cambs

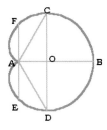

A *New Scientist* editorial on 4 August, 1990, commented on the circles, ruminating on chaos theory, aliens and atmospheric turbulence. This

Professor Gerald Hawkins has analysed the 'Mandelbrot' formation of 1991 for what he calls 'diatonic ratios' and which we'll here treat as simple integer ratios (*The Circular*, June 1993). The core of the formation was a 'cardioid', he argued. This cherry-like shape has the equation $r = 1 + \cos(\Theta)$. It's a fourth-power function, with the intriguing characteristic that for any gradient it has three parallel tangents! Phew, how's that for cereal geometry?

Hawkins' argument starts from the observation, that the swirl-centre of the formation divides the main axis in a 3:5 ratio. This is positioned 'at the mid-point of the Mandelbrot's maximum width' to quote Hawkins. There are buds at the maximum width points C and D, and these are distant six units from the cusp (at A). There are also buds at F and E, which are on the line through the cusp and perpendicular to the main axis. The line FO is five units in length (as likewise is the line BO) which means that FAO is a 3-4-5 triangle. These integer ratios Hawkins saw as having a musical significance.

In the 1960s, Gerald Hawkins published

his ground-breaking *Stonehenge Decoded*, showing its connection with the Sun and Moon. In the 1990s, he has brought the same fearless intellectual integrity to bear upon a no less important mystery.

A letter in the *New Scientist* in 1990 had wondered when this shape would appear in the cornfields.Unfortunately the irate farmer harvested his field as soon as he saw the shape, and so we are rather short of decent overhead-photographs. Professor Mandelbrot commented that he was glad to see his ideas were 'taking root!' This was the first instance of cereal geometry which could not have been made using rope, because of its ever-changing curvature.

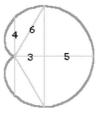

prompted a correspondent on 11 August to ask: "The formations of Corn Circles are growing in complexity each year. How long before we see a complete Mandelbrot set?"

Let's face it, the Circlemakers come up with *knotty* problems. In recent years, formations have been appearing whose mathematical structure would be too bewildering for a school maths course (the East Field fractal of 1998, with its 21 heptagons; the Hackpen Hill vortex pattern of 1999 and the 'semiconductor' of West Kennet with its 800 sectors, in 2000), here omitted. As the millenium turns, Hypermaths is expressing much more complex motifs.

14 May, 2000
Wrotham, Kent

Tri-cycloids
26 May, 2000
Kassel, Germany

A cycloid is the path traced out by a point on the perimeter of a moving wheel – for example, the cardioid. The new millenium saw a cycloid-like formation appear in Germany, which had a pleasantly triune motif. Its inner pattern is called a 'trefoil' and its equation is $r = \sin(3\Theta)$. The outer curve, which is moving round to a different rhythm, has no name but its equation is $r = 5 + \sin(3\Theta/2)$, where r is the radius and Θ is the rotation angle about the centre (Mr N. Thomas kindly found these equations). Again, there is no way this could have been made using ropes, owing to the constantly changing curvature.

The Cushion
19 June, 2000
Windmill Hill, Wilts

Only straight lines at right angles were used to obtain this amazing 3-D effect with a 'rollover' at the edge. This design would make a nice picnic blanket, or flower-garden surrounded by high-rise flats that would gaze down at its dizzy pattern. It has seven concentric squares, whose various sides and lengths form no constant ratio. It was based upon an op-art design of the 1980s, although its proportions were not quite the same, and it seemed somehow more impressive. Michael Glickman described it as 'the most assured expression of graphic three-dimensionality' which the Circle-

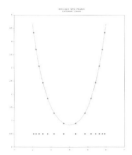

makers had yet given us (SC., August 2000). Walking around it, I noticed a two-foot wide 'edge' corresponding to a half-width portion, which helped to give the 'rollover' effect.

This formation had an odd effect upon cameras and film, and one heard that the local camera shop had several impaired cameras brought in, affected by this formation. This phenomenon was discussed by Freddy Silva on his website and by Francine Blake in her Wiltshire journal, *The Spiral.*

The Wilson op-art book above-mentioned has something resembling this pattern, without explaining its design. We surely ought to assume that something beyond guesswork informed the spacing of its lines. I tried various projections which did not very credibly resemble this design, then finally tried a 'catenary curve'. This is the shape of a chain which hangs under its own weight. One has to divide the curve into equal-length portions, which gives a 'necklace of pearls', then project the spacing of these 'pearls' onto the horizontal. This construction, I found, did exactly match the dimensions on the ground.

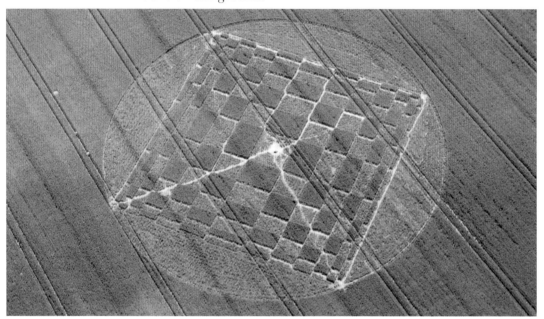

For addicts only: the catenary is given by the hyperbolic function $y = \cosh(x/a)$ or $y = a/2(e^{x/a} + e^{-x/a})$ where a (varying between 0.7 - 0.9 in the diagrams) was equal to 0.83 in this design. The distance along this curve is conveniently given by $\sinh(x/a)$.

Starting off with a triangle, we draw three circles from its corners in the usual manner, using its sides as radii. Then, adding another triangle to make a star-hexagon, we use the full length of that hexagon to draw another three circles, from the corners of the new triangle. That produces three crescent-moons, each having its tip in the centre of an adjacent one. The two sets of circles have their areas in a 3:4 ratio.

Revolving Moons
12 June, 1996
Littlebury Green,
Essex

One may prefer here to use the Pythagorean Tetraktys, because all of its points get used in this remarkable whirling-moon design. Next, we draw a circle that just touches the three crescent moons. Although this circle is not present in the wheat, it links together the inner and outer design, because the three outer dark circles have the same size as this circle.

A hexagon is drawn around this 'liminal' circle to give us the centres of the outer circles. Those three large 'dark' circles are in fact just touching each other, although we are not shown this. What we see is a big, central circle laid down in the wheat as would touch the corners of this 'latent' hexagon. Overall, the formation expresses harmony, symmetry and a whirling motion. The design has a twist to it: the sides of the central hexagon (etched within the Tetraktys pattern we started with) point to the corners of the outer hexagon, and also *en passant* touch the lunar-crescent tips. Phew, how did that happen? The inner-outer relationships here expressed take quite a bit of mulling over. The design's apparent simplicity masks a subtle and complex latent geometry.

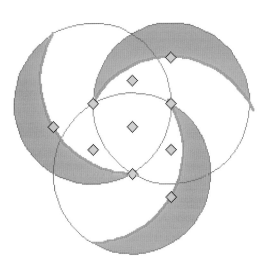

Hopi Moiré
1 August, 2001
Allington, Wilts

A *three-way* interference-pattern was made, dividing the sides of a triangle by fourteen. Let's start by mulling over the diagrams, to get a sense of how form emerges from these triune interference-patterns. The three little central triangles were an essential clue, indicating how circular arcs were creating these shapes.

Word went round the Web that a mistake had been made: two sides had five 'spokes' while the other had only four. A photoshop 'corrected' version appeared, fully symmetrical! This was however an important clue, as 5 + 5 + 4 equals 14, the key number of this design. The Circlemakers don't make mistakes . . .

Ripples spread out from each corner of the triangle, of wave-length that gave *14 waves* per side. There is a fainter second triangle behind the first one, making a hexagon. One part of the star is missing, which may be telling us that what is going on here is an approximation, not perfect symmetry. A fourteen-fold division is being related to the hexagon structure.

Circle-arcs pass through the centre, ½ of the side length, and larger arcs form a boundary to the central figure, just touching the triangle edge. These are ⅚ of a side length, equalling the triangle height within one per cent. Small arcs near the corners, ⅖ of the side-lengths, can be seen to touch the 'hidden' sides of the second triangle. (To avoid possible misunderstanding, the arcs drawn in here were not present in the design, as lines of laid-down corn.)

Conclusion

Professor Gerald Hawkins spoke to the 1998 meeting of the American Astronomical Society at Washington, DC, on the subject 'From Euclid to Ptolemy in English crop circles'. He received a standing ovation. Hawkins had been seeking what he called the 'intellectual profile' of the unknown artist(s): 'the mechanics of how they (the crop patterns) are formed is a mystery,' he concluded, 'but the intellectual profile behind it all has turned out to be an even greater mystery'. He had come to apprehend that, 'Over the years, the circle makers have progressively connected geometry and music.' His views have been outlined in Colin Wilson's *Alien Dawn*, (1999) and Linda Moulton Howe's *Mysterious Lights and Crop Circles* (2000); there is a section on his work in the Crop Circular website.

Hypermaths is concerned with inner response to shape and number, having, after all, much in common with traditions of sacred geometry. As such it would tend to exert a cohesive effect in the modern classroom. Because of the focus of Hypermaths upon design and decorative features, it would help to hold a mathematics class together over the wide ability-range found in modern schools. Hypermaths would be especially suitable for persons going on to do graphic design or architecture, helping the people of the future to see its highest aspirations experienced together.

There is one question which the teacher of Hypermaths would not answer, and that concerns the origin of the formations. A cheerful agnosticism is here required, or the reply that the question belongs to physics and not maths. Nothing would more quickly abort the prospects of Hypermaths than such speculations.

Let's end by shedding a tear for the marvellous formations that were never measured or overhead-photographed for detailed analysis to be feasible, and salute the tireless labours of persons like Andreas Muller and Peter Sorensen logging the data, without whom we would be helplessly prey to the jackals of scepticism.

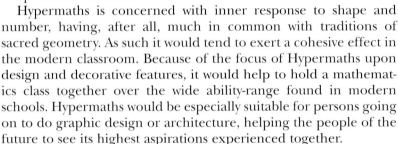

Appendices

Three-quarters of all the formations analysed in this book were laid down within just four years 1997–2000. A wholistic mathematics has manifested in this interval. Only two formations from the year 2001 are here included. I have argued that Hypermaths, or whatever one wants to call it, would be of immediate value in a school classroom, and improve the esteem in which the activity of mathematics was held. It would do this by integrating right- and left-brain components, by bringing spiritual and aesthetic meanings into the subject. Forms have been appearing whose essence appears inherently musical–mathematical, and there seems to be (again, unless I am much mistaken) a sense of delight in the way they have appeared and unfolded.

The alignment of our planet's axis with the Milky Way galaxy has taken place during this period. Let's leave open the door of possibility that, just maybe, this stellar or galactic event is somehow relevant. This is an event which most readers will not have heard of, as it has passed by almost unnoticed; yet it has happened and is now happening, incontrovertibly. To what extent it has any significance for human history remains an open question. There is a steep angle between the great wheel of the galaxy and that of the zodiac, and at their two intersection-points the solstices now take place.

At the solstices, summer and winter, the Sun now stands precisely on the Milky Way meridian-line or equator. That is the simplest way of picturing the alignment. That became exact in 1998, although as it is such a slow-moving event the exact year may not mean very much. It is the only time in human history that it has happened. It has come about in the very moment of human evolution, when the galactic co-ordinates have been mapped out to enable us to ascertain when it would happen. One could view this as being providential.

There was a comparable alignment 13,000 years ago when the Sun at its solstices stood right on the Galactic equator. (The line of

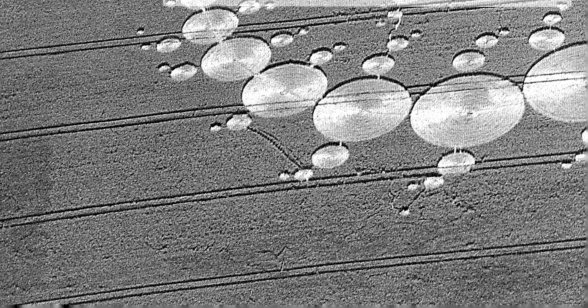

the solstices signifies the direction in which Earth's tilted axis is pointing in space, so that that tilt was then and is now pointing to the intersection-point of the ecliptic and the Galactic plane – astronomically-inclined readers may prefer this view.) I suggested some years ago (*The Circular* Autumn 1997, 'Millenium Galactic Alignment') that this event was relevant to the coming of the crop-circles.

Are we not living at a turning-point of history? A lot of people have wanted to believe that some 'Age of Aquarius' was now dawning, but there are several centuries to go before anything credibly resembling a dawning of Aquarius happens in the heavens. So the attunement or alignment to the Milky Way may be a more workable type of myth, so to speak, because it is indubitably happening in the Heavens.

The diagram shows part of the starry background through which the galaxy's Equator-line passes. Naturally, the centre of the galaxy has to be on that line. It happens (by chance, so to speak) that we see the Galactic core as close to the ecliptic (the line through the middle of the zodiac). This diagram shows the staggering fact that three constellations form a vivid triangle around that centre: the Scorpion's sting, the point of the Archer's arrow, and the foot of the Serpent-Bearer. So this is quite a dramatic and significant part of the heavens. In 1994, various scorpion-type agriglyphs appeared in the fields of Wiltshire (see Goodman, *Crop Circles of Wessex*, 1996), and I'd like to suggest that they all emphasized the large star Antares, Heart of the Scorpion – shown in this diagram.

The vertical line 'zero Capricorn' in the diagram moves slowly across the stars through what is called the 'precession,' moving 1° per 72 years. At the winter solstice, the Sun is at 0° of Capricorn. So these stars in the diagram are the ones we see in summertime, when the Sun is at the other end of the zodiac. That will probably suffice to give us a picture of this unique, galactic event, that happens only once in human history.

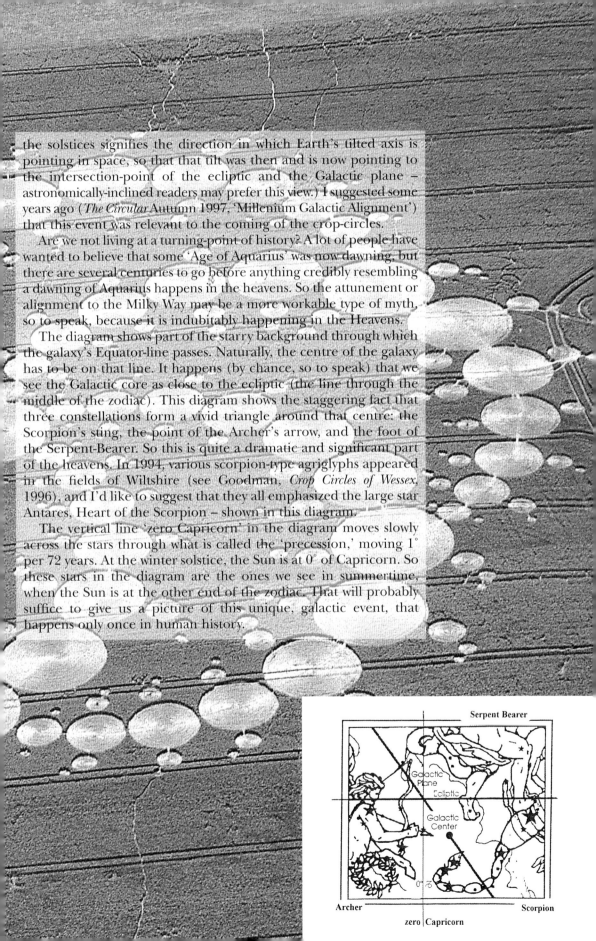

FUN WITH PHI
Making the Golden Ratio

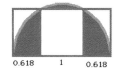

0.618   1   0.618

Put a square in a circle, so that it rests on a diameter and its corners touch the circumference. This makes rectangles in the Golden Ratio phi (Φ) as shown, where

$$\Phi = a/b = (a+b)/a = 1.618 \ldots$$

The circle has diameter $\sqrt{5}$ times the sides of the square. Phi equals *half of one plus the square root of five*. Maths using the Golden Ratio is fun because:

$$\Phi^2 = \Phi + 1 \qquad \text{and} \qquad 1/\Phi = \Phi - 1$$

See if you can show that:

$$2 = \Phi + 1/\Phi^2$$

Presence in the pentagram

We start off using the 'quintile' angle, which is one-fifth of a circle (72°), drawing a triangle with two of these at its base. It therefore has a decile angle (one-tenth of a circle, 36°) at its top. So far we can't see anything special about it. But, let us now bisect one of the base angles, as shown. Now we suddenly apprehend, by similar triangles, that it expresses the Golden Ratio:

$$CB/BA = BD/DA \text{ (similar triangles)}$$

But AC = AB and CD = DB = BA, so CD/DA = CA/CD, the essential definition of the Golden Ratio, Φ. Therefore, AB/CB = Φ QED. We are starting to make the pentagram, with this construction. Thus the pentagram diagonals intersect in Golden Ratios.

   Next, we bisect the original triangle from the top downwards, and are then startled to see that:

the cosine of a quintile is half the Golden Ratio

– the mystic secret at the heart of the pentagram:

$$\cos 72° = AD/AC = 1/2\Phi = (\Phi-1)/2.$$

It can also be shown that $\cos 36° = \Phi/2$, or

$$\Phi = 2\cos(\pi/5).$$

TRIANGLE TRIG.

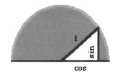

sin

cos

Sine and cosine are the projections, of the unit circle radius, onto the vertical and horizontal. Draw a tangent to the radius, then 'tan' of an angle measured from this, is the length it makes when projected onto that tangent line.

   A triangle of three equal sides ('equilateral'), each of two units length, is bisected, to give a 60-30-90° triangle of sides 2, 1 and $\sqrt{3}$. Then:

$$\sin 30 = \cos 60 = AD/AB = 1/2,$$
$$\cos 30 = \sin 60 = BD/AB = \sqrt{3}/2 = 0.866, \text{ and}$$
$$\tan 30 = DB/AD = 1/\sqrt{3} \text{ and } \tan 60 = \sqrt{3},$$

where $\sqrt{3} = 1.732$.

   Likewise, for the isosceles triangle, 45°–90°–45°, putting its sides equal to 1, 1 and √2 (=1.41):

$$\text{sine } 45° = \cos 45 = 1/\sqrt{2} \text{ and } \tan 45 = 1.$$

Rotations are generally best done using polar co-ordinates, but one can use:

$$x' = x \cos a - y \sin \alpha$$
$$\text{and} \qquad y' = x \sin a + y \cos \alpha,$$

where α is the angle of rotation. To convert polar co-ordinates, with r the radius vector and 1 the angle at the centre, into x, y co-ordinates use:

$$x = r \cos 1, \ y = r \sin 1.$$

Data and Web Access

The database of the UK's Centre for Crop Circle Studies has here been used, as compiled by George Bishop, its journal editor, from 1992 to 1999; it includes those formations which he judged to be reliably dated. The first graph shows the *weekend excess*, whereby 30 per cent more happen on Saturdays and Sundays than on weekdays. There was no excess of Monday sightings over those on Fridays, as could be expected were the excess due to an increased number made over the weekend.

The next graph shows the seasonal trend: the circles begin appearing in mid-April, rising to a peak in late July, and then peter out at the end of August as the crops are harvested, with just a trickle in September. The year-by-year totals remain fairly steady at around 160–165 and don't seem to show any trend.

The website used for this survey was mainly the 'Crop Circle Connector', plus Freddy Silva's excellent 'Crop Circular'. Paul Vigay's 'Crop Circle Research' site plays a major part in contemporary debates. For top-quality gossip visit 'Swirled News,' and don't forget to pay a visit to Martin Keitel's inspiring (Finnish) website especially for his analysis of the heptagon formations. Bert Janssen, who produces award-winning videos, has some of his trenchant mathematical analyses on the *Connector* site.

Visit the website of the Centre for Crop Circle Studies (CCCS) on

cccs-uk.org/index.htm

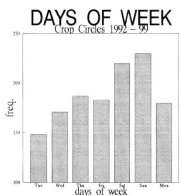

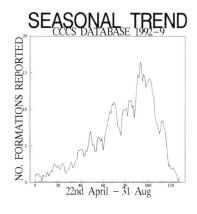

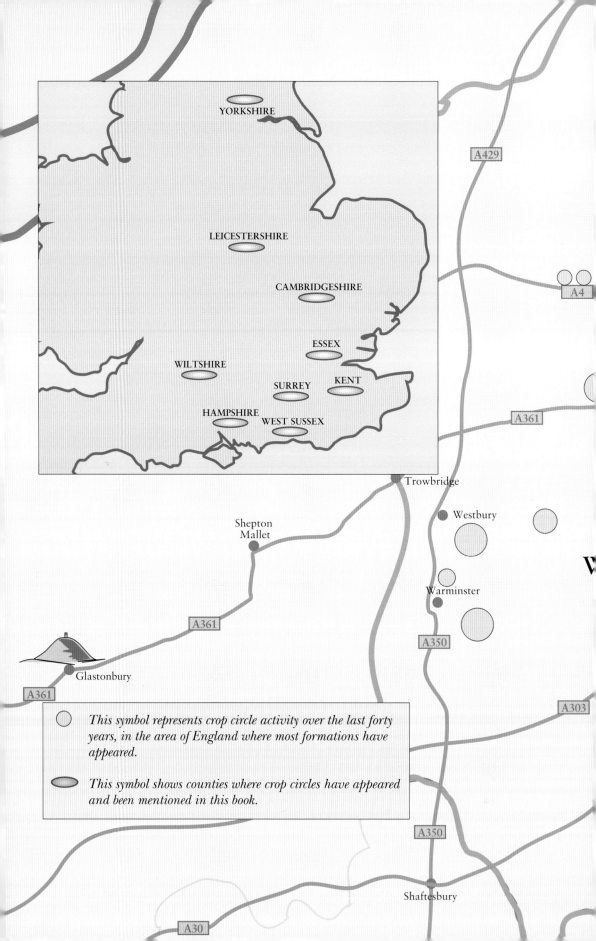

YORKSHIRE

LEICESTERSHIRE

CAMBRIDGESHIRE

ESSEX

WILTSHIRE

SURREY

KENT

HAMPSHIRE

WEST SUSSEX

A429

A4

A361

Trowbridge

Westbury

Shepton
Mallet

Warminster

A361

A350

Glastonbury

A361

A303

This symbol represents crop circle activity over the last forty
years, in the area of England where most formations have
appeared.

This symbol shows counties where crop circles have appeared
and been mentioned in this book.

A350

Shaftesbury

A30

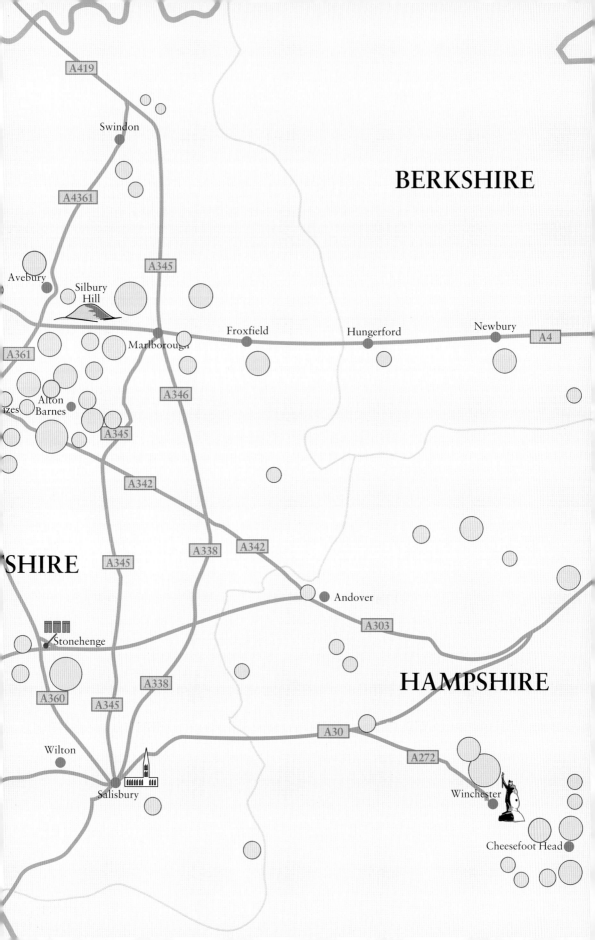

BERKSHIRE

HAMPSHIRE

SHIRE

A419

Swindon

A4361

A345

Avebury

Silbury
Hill

A361

Marlborough

Froxfield

Hungerford

Newbury

A4

A346

Alton
Barnes

izes

A345

A342

A338

A342

A345

Andover

A303

Stonehenge

A338

HAMPSHIRE

A360

A345

A30

A272

Wilton

Winchester

Salisbury

Cheesefoot Head

Bibliography

Keith Critchlow, *Islamic Patterns* Thames & Hudson 1974

E. D. Hodge & B. Wood, *Pure Mathematics* Blackie & Son 1976.

M. Ghyka, *The Geometry of Art and Life* Thames & Hudson NY 1977

Robert Lawlor, *Sacred Geometry* Thames & Hudson 1985

M. Schneider, *A Beginner's Guide to constructing the Universe* Harper Collins 1995

John Martineau, *A Book of Coincidence* Wooden Books 1995, 2000

Andy Thomas, *Vital signs, a Complete Guide to the Crop Circle Mystery* SB Publications 1998

B. Janssen, *Crop circles/research* (video) 1999 ossebard.wxs.nl

S. Alexander & K. Douglas, *Crop Circle Yearbooks Temporary Temple Press* 1999, 2000

John Martineau, *Altair Raindrops* 2000

Related discussion

Here are some science-journal articles:

Terence Meaden, Mystery spirals in a Wiltshire cereal-field *Jnl. Of Meteorology*, 6, 1981, 76-80.

Terence Meaden, Crop-damage patterns by atmospheric vortices, *Weather*, 44, 1989, 2-10.

A. Anderson, Britain's crop circles, *Science*, 253 1991, p.961-2.

G. Hawkins & I. Peterson, Off the Beat: Euclid's Crop Circles, *Science News* 141, 1992, p.76-77.

W. C. Levengood, Anatomical anomalies in crop formation plants, *Physiol Plant.* 92,1994, 356-363.

T. Riese & Y. Chen, Crop circles and Euclidian geometry, *Int. J. Math. Edn. In Sci. & Tech.*, 25, 1994, p.343.

H. Tunis, Geometry in English wheatfields *The Mathematics Teacher* 99, 1995, p.802.

W. C. Levengood & J.A. Burke, *Jnl. Sci. Explor.* 9, 1995, 191-9.

Hawkins, Crop circles: Theorems in wheat fields, *Science News*, 150, 1996, p.239.

Hawkins, From Euclid to Ptolemy in English crop circles, *Bulletin Of the American Astronomical Society*, 29, 1997, p.1263.

Hawkins, Geometry in English wheatfields, *The Mathematics Teacher*, 88, 1995, p.802.

Hawkins, New geometry in English crop circles, *The Mathematics Teacher* 91, 1998, p.441.

W. C. Levengood & N.P. Talbot, Dispersion of energies in worldwide Crop Formations, *Physiol. Plant.* 105, 1999, 615-624.

E. H. Haselhoff, Comment to 'Dispersion of . . .' *Physiol . Plant.* 111, 2000, p124.

P. van Doord, A case of genuine crop circles, *Jnl. Of Meteorol.*, 25, 2000, 20-1.

Hawkins theories are described in *Cosmos* 1992, 1 (Washington DC) 'Probing the Mystery of those eerie crop circles'; and *Mysterious Lights and Crop Circles.* Linda Moulton Howe 2000.